The Tempest

KS3 Shakespeare Pupil Workbook

2008 Set Scenes

PEARSON
Longman

Pearson Education Limited
Edinburgh Gate
Harlow
Essex
CM20 2JE
England
and Associated Companies throughout the World

Play text © Pearson Education Limited 2004

Additional material © Pearson Education Limited 2007

ISBN 978-14058-5644-7

The Publisher's policy is to use paper manufactured from sustainable forests.

Cover photograph: © Donald Cooper/Photostage

Printed in Great Britain by Ashford Colour Press Ltd, Gosport, Hampshire.

CONTENTS

Act 1
The play opens with a dramatic storm. King Alonso of Naples, his son, Ferdinand, and other members of the court, including Antonio, Prospero's brother, are on board a ship that is sailing home. The storm is so bad that the ship splits apart.

On an island nearby, Miranda begs her father, Prospero, to use his magic powers to calm the storm. Prospero reassures her that no one has been harmed. He then tells her that he used to be Duke of Milan until his brother Antonio stole the title from him 12 years ago. He and Miranda were put to sea and ended up on the island. Chance has now brought Antonio close to the island.

Prospero summons his spirit servant, Ariel, and congratulates him on the storm he has created at Prospero's command. Ariel describes what happened on the ship and then asks Prospero to set him free. Prospero reminds him that he had released him from the power of the witch, Sycorax, many years before. Sycorax's son, Caliban, is now a slave to Prospero. He promises Ariel that he will set him free when his work is done.

Miranda awakes and Prospero summons Caliban, who curses Prospero for stealing his island. Then Ariel re-enters, leading Ferdinand, King Alonso's son, who has been washed up on the island. Ferdinand and Miranda are immediately attracted to each other and Prospero makes Ferdinand his slave to test his love for Miranda.

Act 2
On another part of the island, King Alonso believes that his son has drowned and Gonzalo, his old councillor, tries to comfort him. Ariel casts a spell that makes everyone go to sleep, except Antonio and Sebastian, Alonso's brother. Antonio persuades Sebastian to murder Alonso, so that he can replace him as King of Naples. As Sebastian and Antonio are about to kill Alonso and Gonzalo, Ariel makes them all wake up and they decide to go and look further for Ferdinand.

On a different part of the island, Caliban sees Trinculo, King Alonso's jester, and hides beneath his cloak when he hears thunder. Trinculo then also gets under Caliban's cloak for shelter. Stephano, King Alonso's butler, appears, drunk, and on seeing the two figures under the cloak, he thinks he has come across a monster. Stephano gives Caliban some of his wine and Caliban begins to worship Stephano. Caliban then says he will show the other two where to find food and fresh water on the island.

Act 3

Ferdinand has to carry logs for Prospero. Miranda offers to help him and they declare their love for each other. Prospero, who has been secretly watching them, is pleased.

Stephano, Trinculo and Caliban are all drunk. Caliban explains that Prospero has stolen his island and persuades Stephano that he should murder Prospero. Ariel is invisible and speaks in Trinculo's voice, causing the other characters to argue.

King Alonso and his companions are exhausted from wandering around the island and sit down to rest. Prospero and Ariel cause spirits to appear in strange shapes and prepare a banquet. As soon as the noblemen try the food, Ariel appears in the form of a harpy (a terrifying bird of prey with the head of a woman) and reminds Alonso, Antonio and Sebastian of their sins. King Alonso is the only one who expresses remorse.

Act 4

Prospero agrees to allow Miranda to marry Ferdinand. He arranges some entertainment in celebration that is performed by spirits. **Prospero then remembers Caliban's plot to murder him. He sends Ariel to collect some flashy clothes to hang on a line. Caliban, Trinculo and Stephano appear, soaked and dirty from being led by Ariel through a stinking pond. Stephano and Trinculo are distracted by the clothes and are eventually chased away by spirits in the form of hunting dogs, who have been summoned by Prospero.**

Act 5

Prospero tells Ariel it is better to forgive than to take revenge and asks him to fetch Alonso and his companions. Prospero imprisons them in a trance and talks to them each in turn about what they did. Then he reveals who he really is and Alonso asks him for forgiveness. Prospero shows that Ferdinand is safe with Miranda. Ariel leads in the ship's Master and Boatswain, followed by Caliban, Stephano and Trinculo. Prospero promises that everyone will be taken home safely. Finally, Prospero sets Ariel free.

Epilogue

Prospero tells the audience that his spells are all broken now and asks them to release him from the island by applauding the performance.

ACT 3 SCENE 2, WHOLE SCENE

1–39 Stephano and Trinculo are exploring the island with Caliban. They are all drunk and encouraging each other to drink more. Caliban seems to look up to Stephano as his master, while Trinculo mocks Caliban as a monster. Stephano tells Trinculo to be polite and to leave Caliban alone. Ariel appears, but he is invisible to the other characters.

40–79 Caliban tells Stephano and Trinculo that he is a slave to Prospero, who has cheated him out of the island by magic. He wants Stephano to take revenge on Prospero by knocking a nail into his head. During this conversation, Ariel imitates Trinculo's voice and keeps saying that Caliban is a liar. Caliban insults Trinculo and asks Stephano to hit him and take away his bottle. Ariel calls Stephano a liar, again pretending to be Trinculo. Stephano then hits Trinculo.

80–113 Caliban goes on to explain that it is Prospero's habit to have a sleep in the afternoon and that this would be an opportunity to take his books and 'brain him'. He explains that Prospero is powerless without his books. He also tells Stephano and Trinculo that Prospero has a beautiful daughter who would be a good wife for Stephano. Stephano says he will kill Prospero, he and Miranda will be king and queen of the island and Trinculo and Caliban will be deputy rulers. Ariel tells the audience that he will report what he has heard to Prospero.

114–149 Stephano, Trinculo and Caliban then celebrate their plan by singing a song. Ariel, still invisible, plays the tune on a pipe and drum. Stephano and Trinculo are confused and scared by the strange music, but Caliban tells them not to be frightened as the island is often full of delightful noises that make him have wonderful dreams.

ACT 3 SCENE 2, WHOLE SCENE

1. Underline all the words/phrases in this scene that refer to Caliban as a monster or a servant or both.

2. How should Caliban, Stephano and Trinculo enter to show:
- what state they are in?
- the relationships between them?

Another part of the island.

Enter CALIBAN, STEPHANO, *and* TRINCULO.

3. What does this speech suggest about the character and attitude of Trinculo?

STEPHANO	Tell not me! When the butt is out, we will drink water – not a drop before. Therefore bear up, and board 'em. Servant-monster, drink to me.
TRINCULO	Servant-monster! The folly of this island! They say there's but five upon this isle. We are three of them. If the other two be brained like us, the state totters!
STEPHANO	Drink, servant-monster, when I bid thee! Thy eyes are almost set in thy head.
TRINCULO	Where should they be set else? He were a brave monster indeed, if they were set in his tail.
STEPHANO	My man-monster hath drowned his tongue in sack. For my part, the sea cannot drown me. I swam, ere I could recover the shore, five-and-thirty leagues off and on. By this light, thou shalt be my lieutenant, monster, or my standard.
TRINCULO	Your lieutenant, if you list: he's no standard.
STEPHANO	We'll not run, Monsieur Monster.
TRINCULO	Nor go neither – but you'll lie like dogs, and yet say nothing neither.
STEPHANO	Moon-calf, speak once in thy life, if thou beest a good moon-calf.
CALIBAN	(*Very drunk*) How does thy honour? Let me lick thy shoe. I'll not serve *him*. He is not valiant.
TRINCULO	Thou liest, most ignorant monster! I am in case to jostle a constable. Why, thou debauched fish, thou, was there ever man a coward that hath drunk so much sack as I today? Wilt thou tell a monstrous lie, being but half a fish and half a monster?

4. What does this line suggest about Stephano?

5. Pick out three examples of playing on words. For each one, explain the different meanings of the words or phrases. What effect does this wordplay have on the audience?

7a. What does this speech suggest about Trinculo's attitude towards Caliban?

b. How should he say these lines?

6a. What do you notice about the language Caliban uses to address Stephano?

b. Highlight all the other words or phrases he uses to address or describe Stephano in this scene.

Character and motivation		Language of the text	
Ideas, themes and issues		Text in performance	

Text © Pearson Education Limited 2004

6a. What do you notice about the language Caliban uses to address Stephano?

b. Highlight all the other words or phrases he uses to address or describe Stephano in this scene.

8. 'Natural' means 'idiot' here. Who do you think Trinculo is speaking to? What does this comment suggest about his attitude towards Stephano and Caliban?

CALIBAN Lo, how he mocks me! Wilt thou let him, my lord?

TRINCULO 'Lord,' quoth he? That a monster should be such a natural!

CALIBAN Lo, lo, again! Bite him to death, I prithee.

STEPHANO Trinculo, keep a good tongue in your head. If you prove a mutineer – the next tree! The poor monster's my subject, and he shall not suffer indignity.

CALIBAN I thank my noble lord. Wilt thou be pleased to hearken once again to the suit I made to thee?

STEPHANO Marry, will I. Kneel and repeat it. I will stand, and so shall Trinculo.

9. In this scene, Caliban uses other characters to get what he wants. What is Caliban's 'suit'? Go through the rest of the scene and underline all the other references to what he wants Stephano to do.

10a. Where should Ariel position himself when he enters? Think about what he is trying to achieve in this scene.

b. Draw a sketch to show where all the characters could be on stage at this point in the scene.

Enter ARIEL *(invisible).*

CALIBAN As told thee before, I am subject to a tyrant – A sorcerer, that by his cunning hath cheated me Of the island.

ARIEL Thou liest.

CALIBAN (*To* TRINCULO) 'Thou liest,' thou jesting monkey, thou! I would my valiant master would destroy thee! I do not lie.

STEPHANO Trinculo, if you trouble him any more in's tale, by this hand, I will supplant some of your teeth.

TRINCULO Why, I said nothing!

STEPHANO Mum, then and no more. (*To* CALIBAN) Proceed.

11. Annotate these lines, explaining how Stephano should say them to show he is trying to assert control over Trinculo.

12a. What does this choice of words suggest about Caliban's view of Trinculo?

b. List all the words he uses to describe Trinculo in this scene.

CALIBAN I say, by sorcery he got this isle – From me he got it. If thy greatness will Revenge it on him – for I know *thou* dar'st, But this thing dare not –

STEPHANO That's most certain.

CALIBAN Thou shalt be lord of it, and I'll serve thee.

STEPHANO How now shall this be compassed? Canst thou bring me to the party?

CALIBAN Yea, yea, my lord. I'll yield him thee asleep, Where thou may'st knock a nail into his head.

ARIEL Thou liest: thou canst not.

 Character and motivation

Language of the text

 Ideas, themes and issues

Text in performance

13. Highlight all the other words in this scene which suggest the aggressive side of Caliban's character.

14. How does Stephano assert himself here to get what he wants?

17. Caliban repeats himself here. Why does he do this? Use coloured pens to underline or highlight other examples of repetition he uses in this scene. What is the effect in each case?

15. Act out this section or draw a storyboard, showing where each character needs to stand, where they should move and how they should say their lines. If you are acting, try doing it in slow motion and then speeded up.

16. What impression do you have of Stephano here? Which of the following words/phrases best describe him? Self-important, bossy, grumpy, drunk, irritated, powerful, out of control, enjoying himself or angry?

CALIBAN	What a pied ninny's this! (*To* TRINCULO) Thou scurvy patch!
	(*To* STEPHANO) I do beseech thy greatness, give him blows
	And take his bottle from him. When that's gone, He shall drink nought but brine – for I'll not show him Where the quick freshes are.
STEPHANO	Trinculo, run into no further danger! Interrupt the monster one word further, and, by this hand, I'll turn my mercy out o'doors, and make a stockfish of thee.
TRINCULO	Why, what did I? I did nothing! I'll go farther off.
STEPHANO	Didst thou not say he lied?
ARIEL	Thou liest.
STEPHANO	Do I so? Take thou that! (*He hits* TRINCULO.) As you like this, give me the lie another time!
TRINCULO	I did not give the lie! Out o'your wits, and hearing too? A pox o'your bottle! This can sack and drinking do. A murrain on your monster, and the devil take your fingers!
CALIBAN	Ha, ha, ha!
STEPHANO	(*To* CALIBAN) Now, forward with your tale. (*To* TRINCULO) Prithee, stand farther off.
CALIBAN	Beat him enough. After a little time, I'll beat him too.
STEPHANO	(*To* TRINCULO) Stand farther! – (*To* CALIBAN)) Come, proceed.
CALIBAN	Why, as I told thee, 'tis a custom with him I'th'afternoon to sleep. There thou may'st brain him, Having first seized his books – or with a log Batter his skull, or paunch him with a stake, Or cut his wezand with thy knife. Remember First to possess his books – for without them He's but a sot, as I am, nor hath not One spirit to command. They all do hate him As rootedly as I. Burn but his books.
	He has brave utensils – for so he calls them – Which, when he has a house, he'll deck withal. And that most deeply to consider is The beauty of his daughter. He himself Calls her a nonpareil. I never saw a woman But only Sycorax my dam and she – But she as far surpasseth Sycorax As great'st does least.

 Character and motivation   Language of the text

Ideas, themes and issues   Text in performance

18. In this scene, the characters are motivated by their own self-interests. What are Stephano and Trinculo hoping to get out of the plot to kill Prospero?

19. Stephano and Trinculo make up very quickly and easily after their argument. What does this suggest about their relationship?

STEPHANO	Is it so brave a lass?
CALIBAN	Ay, lord. She will become thy bed, I warrant, And bring thee forth brave brood.
STEPHANO	Monster, I will kill this man. His daughter and I will be king and queen – save our graces! – and Trinculo and thyself shall be viceroys. Dost thou like the plot, Trinculo?
TRINCULO	Excellent.
STEPHANO	Give me thy hand. I am sorry I beat thee: but, while thou liv'st, keep a good tongue in thy head.
CALIBAN	Within this half hour will he be asleep. Wilt thou destroy him then?
STEPHANO	Ay, on mine honour!
ARIEL	(*Aside*) This will I tell my master.
CALIBAN	Thou mak'st me merry! I am full of pleasure. Let us be jocund! Will you troll the catch You taught me but while-ere?
STEPHANO	At thy request, monster, I will do reason, any reason. – Come on, Trinculo, let us sing. (*They sing*) Flout 'em and scout 'em, And scout 'em and flout 'em: Thought is free.
CALIBAN	That's not the tune.

ARIEL *plays the tune on a tabor and pipe.*

STEPHANO	What is this same?

21a. What does Caliban's choice of language show about his mood here? Underline the words that help to convey his mood.
b. Why is he in this mood?

20a. What has Ariel been doing since he last spoke in line 72?
b. Why is this an important line and how should Ariel say this line to make sure that the audience take note of it?

 Character and motivation   Language of the text

 Ideas, themes and issues   Text in performance

22. What are Stephano and Trinculo's reactions to hearing Ariel's music? What does this tell us about them?

24a. What impression does Caliban's speech give about the island?

b. What impression do you have of the island from elsewhere in the scene?

TRINCULO	This is the tune of our catch, played by the picture of Nobody!
STEPHANO	If thou beest a man, show thyself in thy likeness! If thou beest a devil, take't as thou list.
TRINCULO	Oh, forgive me my sins!
STEPHANO	He that dies pays all debts. I defy thee! Mercy upon us!
CALIBAN	Art thou afeared?
STEPHANO	No, monster, not I.
CALIBAN	Be not afeared. The isle is full of noises, Sounds and sweet airs, that give delight, and hurt not. Sometimes a thousand twangling instruments Will hum about mine ears – and sometime voices, That, if I then had waked after long sleep, Will make me sleep again. And then, in dreaming, The clouds methought would open, and show riches Ready to drop upon me – that, when I waked, I cried to dream again.

23a. Annotate these lines to show how actors might act out this section.

b. How should Ariel react to Stephano and Trinculo at this point?

25. Why might the audience be surprised by Caliban's use of language in this speech?

26. Think about what each of the characters wants here: Stephano, Trinculo, Caliban, Ariel.

STEPHANO	This will prove a brave kingdom to me, where I shall have my music for nothing.
CALIBAN	When Prospero is destroyed.
STEPHANO	That shall be by and by. I remember the story.
TRINCULO	The sound is going away. Let's follow it, and after do our work.
STEPHANO	Lead, monster. We'll follow. I would I could see this taborer: he lays it on.
TRINCULO	Wilt come? I'll follow, Stephano.

Exeunt.

27a. How should the characters leave the stage to create a good ending to this scene?

b. Draw a sketch, showing the order in which the characters should leave the stage.

 Character and motivation   Language of the text

Ideas, themes and issues   Text in performance

Text   © Pearson Education Limited 2004

ACT 4 SCENE 1, LINES 139–262

139–145 Prospero's entertainment, performed by the spirits for Ferdinand and Miranda, has just ended. He speaks to the audience, remembering the plot that Caliban has devised to kill him with Stephano and Trinculo. He notes that the time has come for the plot to take place and he dismisses the spirits. Ferdinand recognises that Prospero is very agitated and Miranda comments that she has never seen him angry before.

146–166 Prospero tells Ferdinand that the entertainment is over and that the actors were all spirits. He goes on to say that one day the whole world will disappear and that everything ends with death. He admits that he is annoyed, but tells Ferdinand to go to his cell while he has a walk. He then calls Ariel and tells him they must prepare to meet with Caliban.

167–193 Prospero asks where Ariel left the villains, Stephano, Trinculo and Caliban. Ariel explains that they were fired up with drinking and that he led them through bushes to a filthy stinking pond. Prospero congratulates him and tells him to remain invisible and to go and collect some flashy clothing from his cell. Prospero curses Caliban, calling him a devil and says that none of his attempts to educate him have had any effect. Ariel then reappears with the clothing and hangs it up on a line.

194–219 Caliban, Stephano and Trinculo enter, soaked and dirty. Ariel and Prospero are invisible to them. Caliban tells Stephano and Trinculo to tread softly as they are very near to Prospero's cell. Stephano and Trinculo are irritated by the fact that they smell horrible and have lost their bottle of alcohol. Caliban keeps telling them to be quiet and urges Stephano to enter the cell and kill Prospero.

220–250 Trinculo spots the flashy clothes that Ariel has hung on the line and encourages Stephano to try on some of them. Caliban tells them to leave the clothes alone and again urges them to carry out the murder. He warns them that if Prospero wakes up, he will turn them into 'barnacles' or 'apes'.

251–262 Suddenly, spirits in the form of hunting dogs appear and chase Stephano, Trinculo and Caliban away, encouraged by Prospero and Ariel. Prospero announces that he has all his enemies at his mercy. His work is nearly at an end and then Ariel will be free.

ACT 4 SCENE 1 LINES 139–262

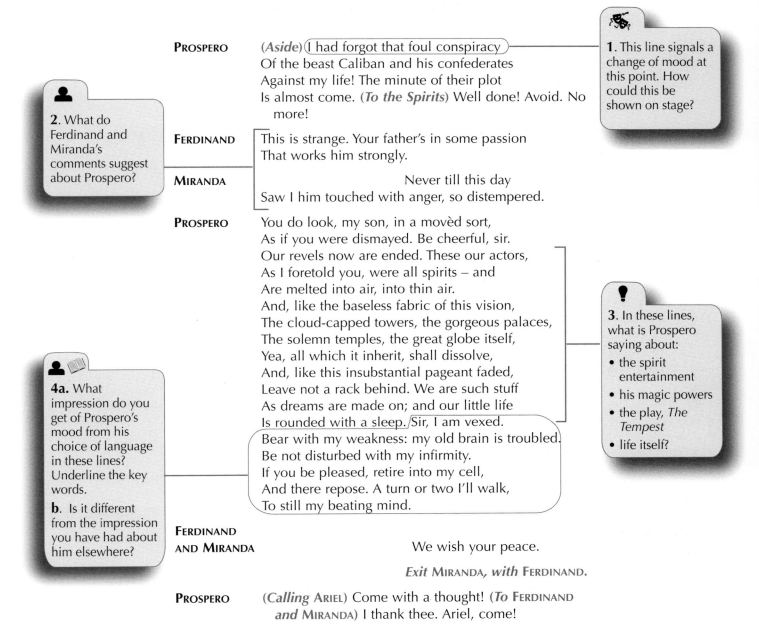

1. This line signals a change of mood at this point. How could this be shown on stage?

2. What do Ferdinand and Miranda's comments suggest about Prospero?

PROSPERO (*Aside*) I had forgot that foul conspiracy
Of the beast Caliban and his confederates
Against my life! The minute of their plot
Is almost come. (*To the Spirits*) Well done! Avoid. No more!

FERDINAND This is strange. Your father's in some passion
That works him strongly.

MIRANDA Never till this day
Saw I him touched with anger, so distempered.

PROSPERO You do look, my son, in a movèd sort,
As if you were dismayed. Be cheerful, sir.
Our revels now are ended. These our actors,
As I foretold you, were all spirits – and
Are melted into air, into thin air.
And, like the baseless fabric of this vision,
The cloud-capped towers, the gorgeous palaces,
The solemn temples, the great globe itself,
Yea, all which it inherit, shall dissolve,
And, like this insubstantial pageant faded,
Leave not a rack behind. We are such stuff
As dreams are made on; and our little life
Is rounded with a sleep. Sir, I am vexed.
Bear with my weakness: my old brain is troubled.
Be not disturbed with my infirmity.
If you be pleased, retire into my cell,
And there repose. A turn or two I'll walk,
To still my beating mind.

3. In these lines, what is Prospero saying about:
• the spirit entertainment
• his magic powers
• the play, *The Tempest*
• life itself?

4a. What impression do you get of Prospero's mood from his choice of language in these lines? Underline the key words.

b. Is it different from the impression you have had about him elsewhere?

FERDINAND AND MIRANDA We wish your peace.

Exit MIRANDA, *with* FERDINAND.

PROSPERO (*Calling* ARIEL) Come with a thought! (*To* FERDINAND *and* MIRANDA) I thank thee. Ariel, come!

 Character and motivation 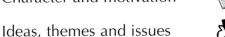 Language of the text

 Ideas, themes and issues  Text in performance

Enter ARIEL.

5. What does this exchange suggest about the relationship between Prospero and Ariel here?

ARIEL	Thy thoughts I cleave to. What's thy pleasure?
PROSPERO	Spirit, We must prepare to meet with Caliban.
ARIEL	Ay, my commander. When I presented Ceres, I thought to have told thee of it – but I feared Lest I might anger thee.

PROSPERO   Say again, where didst thou leave these varlets?

ARIEL   I told you, sir, they were red-hot with drinking –
So full of valour that they smote the air
For breathing in their faces; beat the ground
For kissing of their feet – yet always bending
Towards their project. Then I beat my tabor:
At which, like unbacked colts, they pricked their ears,
Advanced their eyelids, lifted up their noses
As they smelt music. So I charmed their ears,
That, calf-like, they my lowing followed, through
Toothed briers, sharp furzes, pricking gorse, and thorns,
Which entered their frail shins. At last I left them
I'the filthy-mantled pool beyond your cell,
There dancing up to the chins, that the foul lake
O'erstunk their feet.

PROSPERO   This was well done, my bird!
Thy shape invisible retain thou still.
The trumpery in my house, go bring it hither,
For stale to catch these thieves.

ARIEL   I go, I go.

Exit.

6. According to Ariel, how were Stephano, Trinculo and Caliban tricked into following him? Explain in your own words or act it out.

7. Annotate this speech to show how Ariel should say these lines to convey a vivid description. Suggest movements and gestures he could make.

8. How does Prospero plan to trick them now? Is he using magic here? Underline his two instructions to Ariel.

 Character and motivation   Language of the text

Ideas, themes and issues   Text in performance

PROSPERO

> A devil, a born devil, on whose nature
> Nurture can never stick – on whom my pains,
> Humanely taken, all, all lost, quite lost!
> And as with age his body uglier grows,
> So his mind cankers. I will plague them all,
> Even to roaring.

Re-enter ARIEL, with a load of flashy, shining clothing.

> Come, hang them on this line.

Enter CALIBAN, STEPHANO, and TRINCULO, soaked and dirty. (ARIEL and PROSPERO are invisible to them.)

CALIBAN

> Pray you, tread softly, that the blind mole may not
> Hear a foot fall. We now are near his cell.

STEPHANO

> Monster, your fairy, which you say is a harmless fairy,
> has done little better than played the Jack with us.

TRINCULO

> Monster, I do smell all horse-piss – at which my nose
> is in great indignation.

STEPHANO

> So is mine. Do you hear, monster? If I should take a
> displeasure against you, look you –

TRINCULO

> Thou wert but a lost monster.

CALIBAN

> Good my lord, give me thy favour still.
> Be patient, for the prize I'll bring thee to
> Shall hoodwink this mischance. Therefore speak softly.
> All's hushed as midnight yet.

TRINCULO

> Ay, but to lose our bottles in the pool!

STEPHANO

> There is not only disgrace and dishonour in that,
> monster, but an infinite loss.

TRINCULO

> That's more to me than my wetting. Yet this is your
> harmless fairy, monster.

STEPHANO

> I will fetch off my bottle, though I be o'er ears for my
> labour.

CALIBAN

> Prithee, my King, be quiet. See'st thou here:
> This is the mouth o'the cell. No noise, and enter.
> Do that good mischief which may make this island
> Thine own for ever, and I, thy Caliban,
> For aye thy foot-licker.

9a. Find examples of:
- very strong words suggesting evil
- repetition to reinforce a point
- adverbs used for emphasis.

b. How does Prospero's language in these lines show his feelings towards Caliban?

10. Who is leading as these three characters enter and why?

11. What is Stephano and Trinculo's attitude towards Caliban at this point?

12. What is the main thing on Stephano and Trinculo's minds at this point?

13. If you were the director, how would you ask the actors playing Stephano and Trinculo to say these lines? Which words or phrases would you want them to emphasise? Why?

14. What is the main thing on Caliban's mind?

15. Underline the words in Caliban's lines that should be emphasised.

 Character and motivation

Ideas, themes and issues

Language of the text

 Text in performance

Text © Pearson Education Limited 2004

16. How could Trinculo say this line to make it dramatic and funny for the audience?

STEPHANO	Give me thy hand. I do begin to have bloody thoughts.
TRINCULO	O King Stephano! O peer! O worthy Stephano! Look what wardrobe here is for thee!
CALIBAN	Let it alone, thou fool! It is but trash.
TRINCULO	O, ho, monster! We know what belongs to a frippery O King Stephano!

They take and try on the clothes that ARIEL has left.

17. How does Caliban react to the clothes and how do Stephano and Trinculo react? What does this suggest about Stephano and Trinculo?

STEPHANO	Put off that gown, Trinculo. By this hand, I'll have that gown!
TRINCULO	Thy grace shall have it.
CALIBAN	The dropsy drown this fool! What do you mean To dote thus on such luggage? Let't alone, And do the murder first! If he awake, From toe to crown he'll fill our skins with pinches, Make *us* strange stuff.
STEPHANO	Be you quiet, monster. Mistress line, is not this my jerkin? Now is the jerkin under the line: now, jerkin, you are like to lose your hair, and prove a bald jerkin.
TRINCULO	Do, do! We steal by line and level, an it like your grace.
STEPHANO	I thank thee for that jest: here's a garment for it. Wit shall not go unrewarded while I am king of this country. 'Steal by line and level' is an excellent pass of pate! There's another garment for it.
TRINCULO	Monster, come, put some lime upon your fingers, and away with the rest.

18. What does Caliban's choice of language show about his feelings at this point? Is he amused, disappointed, irritated, frustrated, unsurprised, angry, exasperated, bored, or frightened? Explain why.

20. How should the actors move and gesture here to make this section funny for the audience? Think about what Stephano and Trinculo might be doing with the clothes.

 Character and motivation
Ideas, themes and issues
 Language of the text
Text in performance

19. What are Caliban's feelings towards Prospero in this section? Note down key words and phrases in the text.

22. Do you think Prospero and Ariel are enjoying the power that they have at this point?

21. How could this be staged to make it dramatic and entertaining for the audience?

23. Is Prospero justified in using his magic powers in this way? Give a reason for your answer.

CALIBAN	I will have none on't! We shall lose our time, And all be turned to barnacles, or to apes With foreheads villainous low.
STEPHANO	Monster, lay-to your fingers! Help to bear this away where my hogshead of wine is, or I'll turn you out of my kingdom. Go to, carry this!
TRINCULO	And this!
STEPHANO	Ay, and this.

A sudden noise of hunting-horns and dogs. Enter SPIRITS, in the form of large hunting-dogs. They chase STEPHANO, TRINCULO, and CALIBAN to and fro, with ARIEL and PROSPERO shouting to urge them on.

PROSPERO	Hey, Mountain, hey!
ARIEL	Silver! There it goes, Silver!
PROSPERO	Fury, Fury! There! Tyrant, there! Hark, hark!

CALIBAN, STEPHANO, *and* TRINCULO *are chased away.*

Go charge my goblins that they grind their joints
With dry convulsions; shorten up their sinews
With aged cramps – and more pinch-spotted make them
Than pard or cat-o'-mountain!

ARIEL	Hark, they roar!
PROSPERO	Let them be hunted soundly. At this hour Lies at my mercy all mine enemies. Shortly shall all my labours end, and thou Shalt have the air at freedom. For a little Follow, and do me service.

Exeunt.

 Character and motivation   Language of the text

Ideas, themes and issues   Text in performance

The tables on these two pages compare the two set sections by each of the different areas you could be asked about in the test. Each table picks out the similarities between the set sections, giving you questions to think about and highlighting key points for comparison. Use the information in these tables to help you to prepare for the test.

Character and motivation

Act 3 Scene 2 lines 1 – 149	Act 4 Scene 1 lines 139 – 262	Key points for comparison
What do you learn about Stephano and Trinculo from their attitude towards Caliban?	What do you learn about Stephano and Trinculo from their reactions to the flashy clothes?	What impression do you have about Stephano and Trinculo and their relationship and attitude towards Caliban?
What impressions do you have about Caliban's different feelings?	What is Caliban determined to achieve in this scene? What are his feelings towards Stephano and Trinculo?	How far might the audience sympathise with the character of Caliban in these two scenes?

Ideas, themes and issues

Act 3 Scene 2 lines 1 – 149	Act 4 Scene 1 lines 139 – 262	Key points for comparison
Who is trying to achieve what in this scene?	Who thinks that they are in control in this scene? Who is really in control?	Who has power over whom in these scenes?
Who is a 'master' in this scene and who is a 'servant'?	Are there any changes to the 'master'/'servant' roles?	How is the idea of 'master' and 'servant' explored?
What is the role of magic? What are the characters' reactions to the effects of magic?	How is magic used in this scene? Is it used positively or negatively?	In what different ways is magic used in these two scenes and what is the effect of the magic?

Language of the text

Act 3 Scene 2 lines 1 – 149	Act 4 Scene 1 lines 139 – 262	Key points for comparison
How does Caliban's use of language help to convey his feelings in this scene?	What do you learn about Prospero's feelings from his use of language in this scene?	How is language used to convey the feelings of different characters?
What moods are created by the way in which language is used?	How does language help to convey a range of moods in this scene?	How are different moods created in these scenes through the use of language?

Text in performance

Act 1 Scene 2 lines 1 – 149	Act 4 Scene 1 lines 139 – 262	Key points for comparison
How should the actor playing the part of Ariel make the most of his role in this scene?	How should Ariel show his view of Stephano, Trinculo and Caliban?	What advice should a director give to the actor playing Ariel about how to act his part in these scenes?
How should Stephano, Trinculo and Caliban play their parts to make this scene funny for the audience?	How could humour be developed by the actors performing the roles of Stephano, Trinculo, Caliban and Ariel in this scene?	How could these scenes be presented on stage to make them funny for an audience?
How should Caliban play his part to show the different sides of his character?	How should Prospero play his part to show his different feelings at this point in the play?	If you were directing these scenes, how far would you make the audience feel sympathy for Caliban and Prospero?

To do the best you can in the test, you need to be prepared. This section offers guidance on how to prepare for the test. It is divided into four parts: revising the text, the format of the test, the features of a good answer and planning your response.

REVISING THE TEXT

When you revise, you need to make sure you cover everything that will help you in the test. Here are some things to think about that should help you to get the most out of your revision and do your best in the test.

Make sure you know the set sections and how they relate to the play overall.

- *What's the point?* If you only know about the set sections, you may not know why an action or speech is important and may overlook an important point in your answer.
- *How can I check this?* Note where the two set sections occur in the play and in the general timeline of events, what has just happened and what happens next. You can use the summary on pages 4–5 to help you.

Make sure you know how the two set sections relate to each other.

- *What's the point?* The question will involve something common to both sections. Think about what the sections have in common to help you consider what the question might focus on.
- *How can I check this?* Try to work out what the sections have in common or how they reveal different aspects of the characters or themes. The comparison of the set sections on pages 18–19 may help with this.

Make sure you know the characters and how they relate to each other and the play as a whole.

- *What's the point?* Characters that appear in both set sections might feature in the question. Remember that the characters have been invented by Shakespeare, so they act in certain ways and say certain things for a reason. It may be to reveal something about a theme, a character or human nature, for example.
- *How can I check this?* Check which characters appear in each section – they are likely to be main characters and could be the focus of the question.

TOP TIP

Don't forget the characters that appear in one scene and not the other; who enter and then exit; or who speak briefly or remain silent. They may still be important in helping the audience to understand something about the main characters.

Make sure you know the main events and action in each of the set sections.

- *What's the point?* The main events and action are intended to show the audience something about the characters and their motives, or to develop and illustrate the themes of the play.
- *How can I check this?* Read the set sections again and note the key moments, turning points, climaxes or moments of great dramatic significance, or where there is a change of action or mood and atmosphere.

Make sure you know what the key speeches, words and phrases are.

- *What's the point?* If you don't understand what the characters are saying to each other…!
- *How can I check this?* Check those key speeches that illuminate the action/characters/ideas/themes in the scenes and make sure you understand unfamiliar words.

> **TOP TIP**
>
> Don't ignore bits that you've missed or not understood in class. Ask for extra help on these, because 20 lines that you're not sure about could be a large part of one of the extracts in the test. Not understanding this would leave a serious gap in your answer.

THE FORMAT OF THE QUESTION PAPER

It is important to be familiar with how the test is presented – this will mean that you don't get confused and waste time in the test.

This is how the question will be set out in the test. Look at the notes and check you understand what each part means.

General reminder of the characters' situation

The extracts chosen from the set sections for study and a reminder of where they come in the play

The Tempest

Act 1 Scene 2, lines 189–239

Act 5 Scene 1 lines 1–32

In these two extracts, Ariel is acting as Prospero's servant.

What impression would an audience get of Ariel from these two extracts?

Support your ideas by referring to both of the extracts which are printed on the following pages.

The task (always printed in bold)

Shows a focus on character and motivation

Reminder to use quotations and references

Make sure you know that the Shakespeare paper lasts 45 minutes and there will be just one question on the play you have studied.

- *What's the point?* You need to manage your time in the test so that you don't run out of time. Similarly, you don't want to finish with 15 minutes left and an answer that isn't your best.
- *How can I prepare?* Practise and time each of the things you will have to do: reading the question, planning and writing your answer.

Make sure you know the format of the question paper (see opposite page) so that you immediately recognise the question you have to answer and other supporting material.

- *What's the point?* If you know the format you will be able to recognise and use the introductory sentences. These remind you what has been happening in the play and help you understand the questions.
- *How can I prepare?* Practise looking for wording that gives you a clue which of the four areas for assessment the question focuses on. These are: character and motivation; ideas, themes and issues; the language of the text; and the play in performance.

Make sure you know that only about half of each of the set sections for study will be printed as extracts on the paper, with a brief introduction. Focus your answer on these extracts.

- *What's the point?* You need to make sure that your answer focuses on these extracts, not the whole set sections. This amount of text should be manageable in the time available.
- *How can I prepare?* Practise writing detailed comments on 50-line chunks of text so that you learn to develop key points in detail and explain the impact of key words and phrases.

> **TOP TIP**
>
> You should base your answer on the extracts provided in the test, but don't forget everything else you know! Use your knowledge of the rest of the set sections and the play to support your points.

THE KEY FEATURES OF A GOOD ANSWER

Now you know what the test looks like, you need to think about what makes a good answer. Here are some hints on what to do.

Make a plan. This is not time wasted!

- *What's the point?* You can refer to the plan to check that you are always focused on the question and that you have included all the important points.
- *How can I check this?* Practise writing essay plans that you could make in the test – remember that you won't have much time on the day. We will look at planning in more detail on page 24.

Make use of both of the extracts and discuss their content in detail.

- *What's the point?* The extracts have been specifically chosen to provide the key 'raw material' for developing an effective answer.
- *How can I check this?* Write a commentary on two short extracts related to a common character or idea and check that you've covered all key points from both extracts.

Pace yourself. Leave enough time for the second extract!

- *What's the point?* You will lose marks if you refer to only one extract.
- *How can I check this?* Time yourself carrying out the previous check.

Focus on the specific question throughout your answer.

- *What's the point?* Don't just write down everything you know about... whatever! You will not get marks for material that isn't relevant to the question, however much you write.
- *How can I check this?* When you practise writing plans (see above), check that all the points you have listed are relevant to the question.

Use brief, relevant quotations and references to the text to support and develop your answer.

- *What's the point?* Using relevant quotations shows that you really understand and that you are not just repeating half-remembered points from lessons.
- *How can I check this?* When you practise making a plan, find two relevant quotations that provide evidence or support each point you have made.

Don't copy out loads of text for your quotations – just use the most relevant words and short phrases.

Remember to show that you have understood the meaning, themes and impact of the play and not just what happens.

- *What's the point?* This is what this paper is all about!

Try to get your points across clearly.

- *What's the point?* The marker needs to understand the points you are trying to get across in order to decide how well you have understood the play and answered the question.
- *How can I check this?* Practise writing some sample answers with a friend. Then read each other's work and query words, phrases or sentences that don't seem to make sense.

Don't just re-tell the story, or just describe how characters are thinking and feeling. Show how words and actions build up an impression of characters, themes and events to make an impact on the audience.

PLANNING YOUR RESPONSE

Planning is good! It means:

- you can constantly check that you are focused on the question;
- you're not overlooking important points;
- you can check progress against the clock.

When you make a plan you might want to focus on three things. They're not the only things you could pick, but they're a good place to start:

POINT

- The main points from the extracts that address the question and form the backbone of your answer

EVIDENCE

- Key words and phrases from the text that support your points

EXPLORATION

- More detailed comments on characters, themes and events that expand your points and develop your answer

All three things are very important. If you don't include evidence or explorations of your points you will lose marks. If you don't have any points, but just explore what random quotations mean you won't get a very good mark! So when you plan, ask yourself:

- What's my point?
- What is the evidence?
- How can I explain and explore this further?

On the following pages are some practice questions. For each question a series of points, with evidence and explorations, has been completed for you, but for only ONE of the extracts. You should create a similar plan with points, evidence and exploration for the other extract in each case. When you have completed your plan, write your answer to the question.

PRACTICE TASK: ♟ CHARACTER AND MOTIVATION

The Tempest

Act 3 Scene 2, lines 1–78

Act 4 Scene 1, lines 188–252

What impressions do you get of Stephano and Trinculo from the ways in which they speak and behave in these extracts?

Support your ideas by referring to both of the extracts.

An audience might get the impression in the first extract that:

POINT	**Stephano appears to enjoy having Caliban as his servant.**
EVIDENCE	'Therefore bear up, and board 'em. Servant-monster, drink to me'
EXPLORATION	Stephano emphasises that Caliban is his inferior by his use of both 'servant' and 'monster'. This shows that he likes to feel superior.
POINT	**Trinculo is more aware of what is going on than Stephano.**
EVIDENCE	'If the other two be brained like us, the state totters'
EXPLORATION	Trinculo's comment shows that he knows how ridiculous it is that they are all drunk and incapable.
POINT	**Stephano tends to be self-important**
EVIDENCE	'For my part, the sea cannot drown me. I swam, ere I could recover the shore, five-and-thirty leagues off and on'
EXPLORATION	Stephano likes to boast and imagine himself as more significant than he is. He believes that even the sea cannot drown him.

Now plan your response relating to the *second* extract, using POINT, EVIDENCE and EXPLORATION.

PRACTICE TASK: 💡 IDEAS, THEMES AND ISSUES

The Tempest

Act 3 Scene 2, lines 1–105

Act 4 Scene 1, lines 194–250

How is the idea of being in charge and getting what you want explored in these extracts?

Support your ideas by referring to both of the extracts.

In the first extract:

POINT	**Stephano is enjoying the idea of Caliban being his servant in this scene.**
EVIDENCE	'By this light, thou shalt be my lieutenant, monster, or my standard'
EXPLORATION	When he repeats the word 'my', it shows that Stephano, who is a servant himself, is feeling proud of having his own servant.
POINT	**Caliban is willing to serve Stephano, but not Trinculo.**
EVIDENCE	'How does thy honour? Let me lick thy shoe. I'll not serve him. He is not valiant.'
EXPLORATION	'Let me lick thy shoe' suggests he is grovelling to Stephano and will do anything for him, but his rejection of Trinculo is blunt.
POINT	**Trinculo has no time for Caliban at all.**
EVIDENCE	'Lord,' quoth he? That a monster should be such a natural!'
EXPLORATION	He is mimicking Caliban, mocking him for the way in which he looks up to Stephano.

Now plan your response relating to the *second* extract, focusing on POINT, EVIDENCE and EXPLORATION.

PRACTICE TASK: LANGUAGE OF THE TEXT

> ### The Tempest
> Act 3 Scene 2, lines 20–110
> Act 4 Scene 1, lines 139–262
> **How do the characters use language to show their attitudes and feelings at different points in these extracts?**
> *Support your ideas by referring to both of the extracts.*

In the first extract:

POINT	**Trinculo's language towards Caliban is abusive and shows how much he dislikes him.**
EVIDENCE	'Thou liest, most ignorant monster!…Why, thou debauched fish… Wilt thou tell a monstrous lie, being but half a fish and half a monster?'
EXPLORATION	The repetition of the reference to 'monster' and' fish' shows how Trinculo despises Caliban.
POINT	**Caliban in turn has a negative view of Trinculo**
EVIDENCE	'Bite him to death'
EXPLORATION	The use of the word 'bite' shows Caliban's aggressive attitude towards Trinculo.
POINT	**Stephano seems to enjoy telling Trinculo what to do**
EVIDENCE	'Trinculo, keep a good tongue in your head. If you prove a mutineer – the next tree!'
EXPLORATION	Here Stephano's language towards Trinculo seems to be quite dominating and threatening.

> **Now plan your response relating to the *second* extract, focusing on POINT, EVIDENCE and EXPLORATION.**

PRACTICE TASK: 🎭 THE TEXT IN PERFORMANCE

The Tempest

Act 3 Scene 2, lines 1–50

Act 4 Scene 1, lines 214–262

What advice would you give to the actors playing the parts of Stephano, Trinculo, Caliban and Ariel to make these extracts funny for the audience?

Support your ideas by referring to both of the extracts.

In the first extract:

POINT	**When Stephano, Trinculo and Caliban first come on stage, they could be staggering around.**
EVIDENCE	'When the butt is out, we will drink water – not a drop before'
EXPLORATION	Stephano is drunk and determined to drink more. He could be swigging from his bottle and waving it around as he says this in a drunken way, just missing Trinculo's head, which would look comical for the audience.
POINT	**Caliban is so drunk that he is not saying anything and Stephano is trying to get him to speak.**
EVIDENCE	'Moon-calf, speak once in thy life, if thou beest a good moon-calf'
EXPLORATION	Caliban could be so drunk that he is just crawling around, not knowing where he is. I would ask the actor playing Stephano to prod him to make him react as he says these lines.
POINT	**Trinculo should speak to the audience when he is commenting on what is happening. This will help to involve the audience in the comedy.**
EVIDENCE	'Lord,' quoth he? That a monster should be such a natural!'
EXPLORATION	He could roll his eyes and emphasise 'such a natural' to show what he thinks of Caliban.

Now plan your response relating to the *second* extract, focusing on POINT, EVIDENCE and EXPLORATION.